Hamilton Broadway Musical Great Quiz & Facts

Many Amazing Questions and Answers about Hamilton Musical

Copyright © 2020

DEDICATION

Contents

Hamilton (Musical)

Hamilton: An American Musical is a sung-and-rapped-through musical by Lin-Manuel Miranda. It tells the story of American Founding Father Alexander Hamilton. Miranda said he was inspired to write the musical after reading the 2004 biography Alexander Hamilton by Ron Chernow. The show draws heavily from hip hop, as well as R&B, pop, soul, and traditional-style show tunes; and casts non-white actors as the Founding Fathers and other historical figures.[1][2][3] Miranda described Hamilton as about "America then, as told by America now".[4]

From its opening, Hamilton received critical acclaim.[5] It premiered Off-Broadway on February 17, 2015, at the Public Theater, where its several-month engagement was sold out.[6] The musical won eight Drama Desk Awards, including Outstanding Musical. It then transferred to the Richard Rodgers Theatre on Broadway, opening on August 6, 2015, where it received uniformly positive reviews and high box office sales.[7] At the 2016 Tony Awards, Hamilton received a record-breaking 16 nominations and won 11 awards, including Best Musical. It received the 2016 Pulitzer Prize for Drama.

The Chicago production of Hamilton began preview performances at the CIBC Theatre in September 2016 and opened the following month.[8] The West End production opened at the Victoria Palace Theatre in London in December 2017, winning seven Olivier Awards in 2018, including Best New Musical.[9] The first U.S. national tour began in March 2017.[10] A second U.S. tour opened in February 2018.[11] Hamilton's third U.S. tour began January 11, 2019, with a three-week engagement in Puerto Rico featuring Miranda as the titular character, Hamilton

Synopsis

Act I

The orphan Alexander Hamilton experiences a hard early life, and through his smarts, leaves his home, the island of Nevis ("Alexander Hamilton"). In New York in 1776, Hamilton meets Aaron Burr, John Laurens, Marquis de Lafayette, and Hercules Mulligan ("Aaron Burr, Sir"), and impresses them with his rhetorical skills ("My Shot"). The latter three and Hamilton affirm their revolutionary goals to each other, while Burr remains apprehensive ("The Story of Tonight"). Later, the daughters of the wealthy Phillip Schuyler—Angelica, Eliza, and Peggy—go into town and share their opinion on the upcoming revolution ("The Schuyler Sisters"); it is at this time that Samuel Seabury warns everyone about the dangers of Congress while Hamilton disagrees and counters Seabury ("Farmer Refuted"), until King George III insists on his authority ("You'll Be Back"). During the New York and New Jersey campaign, Hamilton accepts a position as George Washington's aide-de-camp despite longing for field command ("Right Hand Man").

At a ball hosted by Phillip Schuyler ("A Winter's Ball"), Eliza falls hopelessly in love with Hamilton, who reciprocates her feelings to the point of marriage ("Helpless"), as Angelica suppresses her own feelings for the sake of their happiness ("Satisfied"). After the wedding, Burr and Hamilton congratulate each other's successes

("The Story of Tonight (Reprise)") while Burr reflects on Hamilton's swift rise while considering his own more cautious career ("Wait For It").

As conditions worsen for the Continental Army ("Stay Alive"), Hamilton aids Laurens in a duel against Charles Lee, who had insulted Washington ("Ten Duel Commandments"). Laurens injures Lee, who yields, while Hamilton is temporarily suspended by Washington over the duel and is sent home ("Meet Me Inside"). There, Eliza reveals that she is pregnant with her first child, Philip, and asks Hamilton to slow down to take in what has happened in their lives ("That Would Be Enough"). After Lafayette persuades France to get involved on the colonists' side, he urges Washington to call Hamilton back to help plan the final Battle of Yorktown; Washington agrees ("Guns and Ships") but explains to Hamilton—who is convinced he should die a martyr and a hero in war—that he should be careful with his actions because whatever he does will be known for ages to come ("History Has Its Eyes on You"). At the Battle of Yorktown, Hamilton meets up with Lafayette to take down the British, revealing that Mulligan was recruited as a spy, helping them figure out how to trap the British and win the war ("Yorktown

(The World Turned Upside Down)").

Soon after the victory at Yorktown, King George asks the newborn America how it will succeed on its own ("What Comes Next?"), while Lafayette returns to France with plans to inspire his people to have their own revolution. Hamilton's son Philip is born, while Burr has a daughter, Theodosia, and the two tell their children how they will do anything to protect them ("Dear Theodosia"). Hamilton receives word that his long-time friend John Laurens has been killed in a seemingly pointless battle after the war was won and throws himself into his work ("Tomorrow There'll Be More of Us"). He co-authors The Federalist Papers and is selected as Secretary of the Treasury by newly elected President Washington, amidst Eliza begging Hamilton to stay and Angelica moving to London with her new husband ("Non-Stop").

Act II

Thomas Jefferson returns to America from being the U.S. ambassador to France, taking up his newfound position as Secretary of State, with friend and fellow Cabinet member, James Madison ("What'd I Miss"). In 1789, Jefferson and Hamilton debate

Hamilton's financial proposals at a Cabinet meeting. Washington tells Hamilton to figure out a compromise to win over Congress ("Cabinet Battle #1").

Eliza and her family—along with Angelica, back from London—travel upstate during the summer, while Hamilton stays home to work on the compromise ("Take a Break"). Hamilton begins an affair with Maria Reynolds, making him vulnerable to her husband's blackmail ("Say No To This"). Hamilton, Jefferson, and Madison create the Compromise of 1790 over a private dinner, exchanging Hamilton's financial plan for placing the country's permanent capital on the Potomac River. Burr is envious of Hamilton's sway in the government and wishes he had similar power ("The Room Where It Happens"). Burr switches political parties and defeats Philip Schuyler, making Hamilton now a rival ("Schuyler Defeated").

In another Cabinet meeting, Jefferson and Hamilton argue over whether the United States should assist France in its conflict with Britain. President Washington ultimately agrees with Hamilton's argument for remaining neutral ("Cabinet Battle #2"). In the wake of this, Jefferson, Madison, and Burr decide to join forces to find a way to discredit Hamilton ("Washington on Your Side"). Washington decides to retire from the presidency, and Hamilton assists in writing a farewell address ("One Last Time").

A flabbergasted King George receives word that George Washington has stepped down, and will be replaced by Paris signatory John Adams ("I Know Him"). Adams becomes the second President and fires Hamilton, who, in response, publishes an inflammatory critique of the new president ("The Adams Administration"). Jefferson, Madison, and Burr confront Hamilton about James Reynolds' blackmail, accusing him of "[embezzlement of] government funds", which forces Hamilton to reveal his affair with Maria ("We Know"). Out of fear that the affair will be used against him in his political career, Hamilton chooses to publicize his affair ("Hurricane") in the

Reynolds Pamphlet, causing uproar in his political position ("The Reynolds Pamphlet") and damaging his relationship with Eliza, who, in a heartbroken retaliation, burns all the letters Hamilton wrote her, trying to erase herself from history ("Burn"). After graduating college, Philip attempts to defend his father's honor in a duel with George Eacker ("Blow Us All Away") but is fatally shot ("Stay Alive (Reprise)"), causing a reconciliation between Alexander and Eliza ("It's Quiet Uptown").

Hamilton's endorsement of Jefferson in the 1800 election ("The Election of 1800") results in further animosity between Hamilton and Burr, who challenges Hamilton to a duel via an exchange of letters ("Your Obedient Servant"). Hamilton writes his last letter in a rush while Eliza tells him to go back to bed ("Best of Wives and Best of Women"). Burr and Hamilton travel to New Jersey for the duel. Burr reflects on the moments leading up to the duel, stating that one of them will have to die. Burr and Hamilton walk the requisite ten paces, with Burr firing first, and time freezes as Hamilton reflects on his legacy, before throwing away his shot. Burr shoots him between the ribs and Hamilton eventually dies, mourned upon by Eliza, Angelica, and the rest of the cast. Burr laments that though he survived, he is cursed to be remembered as the villain who killed Hamilton ("The World Was Wide Enough").

The musical closes with a reflection on historical memory. Jefferson and Madison reflect on Hamilton's legacy, as Eliza tells how she keeps Hamilton's legacy alive through interviewing war veterans, getting help from Angelica, raising funds for the Washington Monument, speaking out against slavery, and establishing the first private orphanage in New York City ("Who Lives, Who Dies, Who Tells Your Story"). As the musical ends, Eliza looks in the direction of the audience and lets out a tearful gasp.

"Hamilton" Lyrics Quiz

1. In which song does Hamilton speak the following line: "You're absolutely right, John should have shot him in the mouth, that would have shut him up"?

- Meet Me Inside
- Hurricane
- Dear Theodosia
- Best of Wives and Best of Women

2. From which song does the following line come: "Don't modulate the key then not debate with me"?

- Cabinet Battle #2
- The Room Where It Happens
- Farmer Refuted
- What Comes Next

3. The fourth "Duel Commandment" details a number of things that should be done with a doctor in preparation for a duel. Which of the

following is *not* mentioned?

- Double-check his utilities
- Treat him with civility
- Pay him in advance
- Have him turn around to have deniability

4. Who declares that he is "taking this horse by the reins, making redcoats redder with bloodstains"?

- Alexander Hamilton
- Thomas Jefferson
- Aaron Burr
- Marquis de Lafayette

5. In which song does King George declare, "they will tear each other into pieces, Jesus Christ this will be fun"?

- Farmer Refuted
- What Comes Next

- I Know Him
- You'll Be Back

6. Complete this line from "Satisfied", sung by Angelica: "Intelligent eyes in a hunger-pang frame, and when you said 'Hi' _____"

- It felt just like a game
- You set my heart aflame
- I have never been the same
- I forgot my dang name

7. From which song do the following lyrics come: "I'm in the cabinet, I am complicit in watching him grabbing at power and kiss it, if

Washington isn't gon' listen to disciplined dissidence, this is the difference, this kid is out"?

- Washington on Your Side
- Blow Us All Away
- Cabinet Battle #1
- The World Was Wide Enough

8. In which song does line, "Yo, I'm a tailor's apprentice, And I got y'all knuckleheads in loco parentis" appear?

- My Shot
- What'd I Miss
- A Winter's Ball
- Who Lives, Who Dies, Who Tells Your Story

9. Which song begins, "There are moments that the words don't reach. There is suffering too terrible to name"?

- The Election of 1800

- The Reynolds Pamphlet
- Blow Us All Away
- It's Quiet Uptown

10. As the final question, it seems appropriate to ask: What is the final line of "Hamilton"?

- Have I done enough?
- Will they tell your story?
- Who tells your story?
- You really do write like you're running out of time

ANSWER:

1. In which song does Hamilton speak the following line: "You're absolutely right, John should have shot him in the mouth, that would have shut him up"?

Answer: Meet Me Inside

In "Meet Me Inside" George Washington orders Alexander Hamilton to return home from the war. John Laurens shot Charles Lee in the waist during their duel, and in this line Hamilton demonstrates his lack of remorse for permitting the duel to occur.

2. From which song does the following line come: "Don't modulate the key then not debate with me"?

The correct answer was Farmer Refuted

In this song, Samuel Seabury argues against the revolution. Hamilton interjects and attempts to debate with him. This is one of multiple instances in "Hamilton" where the characters show awareness of the music: the score does, indeed, modulate up a half-step just prior to this line.

3. The fourth "Duel Commandment" details a number of things that should be done with a doctor in preparation for a duel. Which of the following is *not* mentioned?
The correct answer was Double-check his utilities

The "Ten Duel Commandments" recur throughout the musical. In total, there are three duels: Laurens vs Lee; Phillip Hamilton vs George Eacker; and, of course, Alexander Hamilton vs Aaron Burr. Having the doctor "turn around to have deniability" is a means of protecting the doctor - if his back is turned, he can honestly say he didn't witness anything. Paying him in advance and treating him with civility are sensible if you want the doctor to do his best to treat you if necessary.

4. Who declares that he is "taking this horse by the reins, making redcoats redder with bloodstains"?

The correct answer was Marquis de Lafayette

This line comes from "Guns and Ships", a song that requires Lafayette to rap at breakneck speed. Lafayette convinces Washington that, if they are to win at Yorktown, Hamilton must take the lead. In the original Broadway production, Daveed Diggs played Lafayette in Act 1 and Jefferson in Act 2. He won the Tony for Best Supporting Actor in a Musical.

5. In which song does King George declare, "they will tear each other into pieces, Jesus Christ this will be fun"?

The correct answer was I Know Him

King George appears on stage for a mere nine minutes, yet manages to squeeze in three songs. In "I Know Him", King George discovers that John Adams is to be the new President of the United States. King George is very critical of the Americans seeking independence and believes they would be better off under his rule.

6. Complete this line from "Satisfied", sung by Angelica: "Intelligent eyes in a hunger-pang frame, and when you said 'Hi' _____"

The correct answer was I forgot my dang name

In the previous song, "Helpless", we see Alexander and Eliza meet for the first time. In "Satisfied", we rewind back in time (the characters move backwards and the turntable in the floor spins in the opposite direction) and view the scene from Angelica's point of view. This ties into the musical's overall theme that everybody will have a different version of history and how things happened. "I forgot my dang name" refers, on the surface, to the euphoric feeling of attraction, but it also reflects Angelica momentarily forgetting that she is a Schuyler and has familial responsibilities to marry rich, as she realises later in the song. In real life, however, Angelica was not the eldest Schuyler child and, indeed, was already married when she met Alexander.

7. From which song do the following lyrics come: "I'm in the cabinet, I am complicit in watching him grabbing at power and kiss it, if Washington isn't gon' listen to disciplined dissidence, this is the difference, this kid is out"?

The correct answer was Washington on Your Side
It is during this moment that Thomas Jefferson realises that he must resign from the Cabinet. This passage uses a dactylic meter (a stressed syllable followed by two unstressed syllables) along with internal false rhyme, assonance and alliteration. Dactyls, a relatively uncommon meter, are also used in Lafayette's blistering rap: "No one has more resilience or matches my practical tactical brilliance". This serves as a reference to the fact that Lafayette and Jefferson is a dual role, played by one actor.

8. In which song does line, "Yo, I'm a tailor's apprentice, And I got y'all knuckleheads in loco parentis" appear?

The correct answer was My Shot

This is how Hercules Mulligan introduces himself. "Loco parentis" is Latin for "in the place of parents". This has a double-meaning in the show: he is saying that he views his friends as parental figures, but it also refers to the notion of Founding Fathers.

9. Which song begins, "There are moments that the words don't reach. There is suffering too terrible to name"?

The correct answer was It's Quiet Uptown

This heartbreaking song details the grief of Alexander and Eliza following the death of their son, Phillip. Together, they slowly begin to piece their lives back together as Eliza forgives Alexander for his adultery. The following song begins with Jefferson asking "Can we get back to politics?", which offers the audience a reprieve from the confronting emotions of "It's Quiet Uptown".

10. As the final question, it seems appropriate to ask: What is the final line of "Hamilton"?

The correct answer was Who tells your story?

All of these lines come from the show's final song, "Who Lives, Who Dies, Who Tells Your Story". The show ends with the cast directly asking the audience who tells their stories. This musical ends in an emotional, tender way. While there are harmonies and orchestrations throughout the song, the final word is sung a cappella and as a single, unified note.

How Well Do You Know the Musical "Hamilton"?

1. Who was Alexander Hamilton?

- Treasury Secretary

- A General

- Secretary of State

- A Singer

2. Which of the listed characters don't re-appear onstage in Act Two?

- Hercules Mulligan and John Laurens

- John Laurens, Marquis de Lafayette and John Jay

- Marquis de Lafayette and James Madison

- John Laurens, Hercules Mulligan, and Marquis de Lafayette

3. In the title song, "Alexander Hamilton", two people say "we fought with him". Who were they?

- James Madison and John Jay

- Benjamin Franklin and James Jay

- Marquis de Lafayette and Hercules Mulligan

- Hercules Mulligan and Philip Schuyler

4. Which song in "Hamilton" has a section that is the fastest sung song on Broadway?

- Guns and Ships

- My Shot

- Ten Duel Commandments

- Cabinet Battle #1

5. Who did Alexander Hamilton have his infamous affair with?

- Angelica Schuyler
- Maria Reynolds
- Eliza Reynolds
- Julia Roberts

6. In the song "Blow Us All Away", Philip Hamilton is seeking to confront a man who publicly defamed his father, Alexander. Who was he?

- John Laurens
- Aaron Burr
- George Eacker
- John Jay

7. What is the final song in Act One?

- Who Lives, Who Dies, Who Tells Your Story
- Blow Us All Away

- History Has Its Eyes On You
- Non-Stop

8. According to Act Two of the musical, why did Aaron Burr challenge Alexander Hamilton to a duel?

- Hamilton published lies about Burr
- Hamilton teamed up with James Madison to keep Burr from becoming president
- Hamilton had an affair with Burr's wife
- Hamilton supported Jefferson in the Election of 1800 and not Burr

9. Which song does King George III NOT sing?

- Farmer Refuted
- What Comes Next
- You'll Be Back
- I Know Him

10. Who are the two characters that sing "One Last Time"?

- Marquis de Lafayette and Alexander Hamilton
- George Washington and Alexander Hamilton
- Thomas Jefferson and Alexander Hamilton
- Eliza Schuyler and Alexander Hamilton

ANSWER

1. Who was Alexander Hamilton?

The correct answer was Treasury Secretary

He was the very first Secretary of the Treasury, to be exact. He acted as George Washington's right hand man during the American Revolution, and after the war he was promoted to create a national bank.

2. Which of the listed characters don't re-appear onstage in Act Two?
Answer: John Laurens, Hercules Mulligan, and Marquis de Lafayette

John Laurens dies in battle during the Revolution, Marquis de Lafayette went back to France after the Revolution, and Mulligan just was written out of the play after that point because he didn't do much after the Revolution.

3. In the title song, "Alexander Hamilton", two people say "we fought with him". Who were they?

The correct answer was Marquis de Lafayette and Hercules Mulligan

Lin Manuel Miranda was very sneaky with this line because in Act One, Lafayette and Mulligan physically fight with Hamilton in the revolution, but the actors who play them in the original production also play Jefferson and Madison in Act Two, who also verbally fought with Hamilton.

4. Which song in "Hamilton" has a section that is the fastest sung song on Broadway?

The correct answer was Guns and Ships

Lafayette spits out 19 words in 3 seconds (6.333 words per second) in this song in Act One. The song previously holding that fastest song title was "Not Getting Married Today" from the musical "Company", which had 6.2 words per second.

5. Who did Alexander Hamilton have his infamous affair with?
The correct answer was Maria Reynolds

He cheated on his wife, Eliza, and was blackmailed by James Reynolds (Maria's husband) and Hamilton paid him off. He was caught sending Mr. Reynolds money and was accused of sending government funds (because he was Secretary of the Treasury, so he had access to government funds) and he was forced to publicly publish and admit his affair.

6. In the song "Blow Us All Away", Philip Hamilton is seeking to confront a man who publicly defamed his father, Alexander. Who was he?

The correct answer was George Eacker

Philip called Mr. Eacker out on publicly defaming his father and challenged him to a duel that took place in New Jersey. Philip was shot by Mr. Eacker and later died.

7. What is the final song in Act One?

The correct answer was Non-Stop

"Non-Stop" ends the First Act. The song begins with Hamilton completing a degree at King's College, and he and Burr, become lawyers in New York. Hamilton uses his skills with a quill and his knowledge from being a lawyer to defend the United States Constitution. He wrote the Federalist Papers with James Madison and John Jay and, as the title states, he was "Non-Stop". Hamilton wrote a total of 51 essays defending the document in 6 months.

8. According to Act Two of the musical, why did Aaron Burr challenge Alexander Hamilton to a duel?

The correct answer was Hamilton supported Jefferson in the Election of 1800 and not Burr

Hamilton showed his support for Jefferson, despite being closer with Burr. Burr saw this act as the reason he lost the election, and challenged Hamilton to a duel through letters that were sent back and forth between the two. This can be heard in the song "Your Obedient Servant" in Act Two.

9. Which song does King George III NOT sing?

The correct answer was Farmer Refuted

He sings two songs in Act One, "You'll Be Back" and "What Comes Next?" and one song in Act Two, "I Know Him". "Farmer Refuted" is sung by his loyal defender, Samuel Seabury, in Act One, delivering notice that the King doesn't approve of the Revolution.

10. Who are the two characters that sing "One Last Time"?
The correct answer was George Washington and Alexander Hamilton

This is the song that George Washington sings when he tells Hamilton that he is stepping down from his position as president.
Fun Fact: In the song, both Hamilton and Washington recite George Washington's actual farewell address word for word during this song.

10 Picture Questions about "Hamilton"

1. Which historian wrote the 2004 biography "Hamilton" that inspired the creation of "Hamilton: An American Musical"? (Look at the sphere in the picture and consider other words to describe it to lead you to the correct answer.)

- David McCullough
- Peter Petre
- Stephen Ambrose
- Ron Chernow

2. Lin-Manuel Miranda is certainly a name that has come up in connection with "Hamilton". Which role did he play in both the off-Broadway production and the original Broadway cast? (Consider the place that is shown in this stamp--if you look closely, you can see its

name--and who might have a connection with it.)

- Alexander Hamilton

- Thomas Jefferson

- George Washington

- Aaron Burr

3. In the musical, Hamilton was a resident of which state? (Look at the stamp and you see an image of a bridge at the border of Ontario and this state.)

- Massachusetts

- South Carolina

- Virginia

- New York

4. Leading up to the Battle for New York in 1776, Hamilton joined the Continental Army hoping to see action in battle and perhaps a battle command. On whose staff did he instead serve? (Whose image do you see in this stamp? He is one of the most common people to appear on US stamps.)

- Nathaniel Greene

- George Washington

- Benedict Arnold

- Horatio Gates

5. Ambitious to rise in the world, Hamilton married one of the daughters of the wealthy Schuyler family. Which one? (Who do you see in this stamp?--A bit of translation might help.)

- Eliza

- Cornelia

- Angelica

- Peggy

6. One of the best places to read Hamilton's thoughts on government--especially the US Federal Government--is in "The Federalist Papers". He worked with two other collaborators. Which man did not work with him on this project? (As a hint, consider what is clearly marked on this man, what this is called, and look at the four

answers.)

- All three worked with him
- James Madison
- Aaron Burr
- John Jay

7. With the US Constitution ratified, Hamilton was offered a position in the first President's cabinet despite his wife's concerns (as mentioned in "Non Stop"). Which one? (Look at the type of stamp that is shown. Which government department might have a connection to it?)

- Secretary of State

- Secretary of the Treasury

- Secretary of War

- Attorney General

8. In the musical (and in real life) who succeeded Washington as the second president of the United States? (Look at what is on the stamp and think about with which part of the US that object is associated.)

- James Madison

- Alexander Hamilton

- John Adams

- Thomas Jefferson

9. The Election of 1800 dragged on and on as there was no clear victor as referenced in the song "The Election of 1800". When the election went to the House of Representatives, which candidate did Hamilton throw his support behind? (Consider the person that would be associated with the location shown on the stamp.)

- Aaron Burr

- Thomas Jefferson

- John Adams

- John Laurens

10. In the musical, how did Hamilton die? (Look at the stamp.)

- He is stabbed

- He drowns

- He is shot

- He dies of old age

ANSWER:

1.

The correct answer was Ron Chernow

If you think of a sphere as "round", you might have guessed the correct answer was "Ron" Chernow (a sounds similar clue). Born in 1949, Ron Chernow has written several other biographies including ones about John D. Rockefeller and George Washington (for which he won the Pulitzer Prize). His biography about Alexander Hamilton spent three months on the New York Times bestseller list. Ron Chernow served as a historical consultant for the production of the musical.

2.

The correct answer was Alexander Hamilton

Born in 1980, Lin-Manuel Miranda is a native New Yorker of Puerto Rican descent. In addition to playing the title role, Miranda also wrote the book, lyrics, and music for the show. Best known for "Hamilton", Miranda also wrote the 2012 musical "Bring It On". The place in the stamp is Columbia University, which Hamilton attended. Burr attended Princeton, Jefferson attended William and Mary, and Washington did not attend college.

3.

Answer: New York

Hamilton moved from the West Indies to New York City as a teenager to attend Kings College (now Columbia University). In real life, as in the musical, Hamilton was part of an artillery company that participated in the defense of New York City in 1776. Hamilton later signed the Constitution as a delegate from New York. The Niagara Falls Bridge spans from Ontario to New York

4.

The correct answer was George Washington

The stamp was part of a early 20th century series that all had an image of George Washington. The song "Right Hand Man" refers to this event. Hamilton received the rank of Lieutenant Colonel in his role where he served Washington as an emissary in many functions. Hamilton finally got his desired battle command when he was assigned to lead a light infantry battalion at the Battle of Yorktown in 1781, where he acquitted himself well.

5.

The correct answer was Eliza

The stamp shows Queen Isabella of Spain. Isabella is Spanish for Elizabeth. Elizabeth Schuyler was usually referred to as Eliza in the musical. Elizabeth Schuyler (1757-1854) lived to be almost 100 and outlived Hamilton by 50 years. Elizabeth and Hamilton had eight children together. After his death, she was heavily involved in preserving his legacy and also in various charitable works. The relationship of Eliza and Hamilton is a major theme of the musical.

6.

Answer: Aaron Burr

The initial purpose of "The Federalist Papers" was to convince the voters of New York State to ratify the US Constitution. Alexander Hamilton was the most active member of the three, writing more than half of the 85 essays in the collection. James Madison (1751-1836) was also active, writing a significant number including the famous Number 10 which describes how the Constitution will weaken the spirit of faction. John Jay (1745-1825) only wrote five of the essays, but can be excused as he suffered from a sickness during much of the period (1787-1788) when the essays were written. In the musical, Hamilton approaches Burr to join the collaboration, but Burr turns him down. Aaron Burr (1756-1836) in real-life was an important anti-Federalist in New York. In the drawing, I hoped that you would notice that the man's stomach muscles or "abs" were emphasized and that "ab" would get you to "A"aron "B"urr.

7.

The correct answer was Secretary of the Treasury

Hamilton's once and future rival Thomas Jefferson (1743-1826) was Secretary of State. Henry Knox (1750-1806) was Secretary of War. Edmund Randolph was Attorney General. All four men served under George Washington. From those who supported Hamilton and those who supported Jefferson developed the First Party System of the United States: Federalist v. (Democratic-)Republican. The stamp is a "Revenue Stamp". I hoped that revenue would get you to think about money and money would get you to think about the Treasury.

8.

The correct answer was John Adams

In real life, Jefferson was the third president and Madison was the fourth. Hamilton himself never served as President and as much the musical might show us Hamilton's good side, I think Hamilton would have been hard pressed to have won enough votes even from the restricted electorate of the late 1700s and early 1800s. The song "The Adams Administration" reflects the real-life coolness of relations between Hamilton and Adams. The stamp shows the "Mayflower" which landed at Plymouth which is now part of Massachusetts (home state of John Adams.)

9.

The correct answer was Thomas Jefferson

As originally established by the Constitution, each state had a number of electors based on the number of representatives and senators sent to Congress. Each elector was chosen in a manner of the state's choosing (popular vote, appointment by the state legislature, etc.). Each elector voted for two choices (presumably one was for president and one for vice president). The candidate with the most votes would be president and the candidate with the second most votes would be vice president. In 1796, the president (John Adams) and vice president (Thomas Jefferson) belonged to different parties. In 1800, two candidates from the same party (Jefferson and Aaron Burr) received the same number of votes and more than any other candidate. The election then went to the House of Representatives where each state's delegation had one vote. Hamilton felt that Jefferson was a better choice than Burr to be president and was able to convince enough representatives to change their votes or not vote to allow Jefferson to win. The stamp shows the Louisiana Purchase which occurred during Jefferson's presidency.

10.

Answer: He is shot

In Weehawken, NJ, in 1804, Hamilton and Burr fought their famous duel. Hamilton purposely shot his pistol into the air while Burr's shot wounded Hamilton fatally. There is irony to Hamilton's often repeated line "I am not throwing away my shot." Yet, Hamilton is far more positively remembered today than Burr is.

Trivia Quiz - 15 "Hamilton" Trivia

1. The line "death doesn't discriminate/between the sinners and the saints/it takes and it takes" appears first in which song?

- Say No to This
- Burn
- The World Turned Upside Down
- Wait for It

2. Ham4Ham is a lottery system in which cast members sell front-row tickets for what amount of money?

- $100
- $5
- $10
- $20

3. Lin-Manuel Miranda started writing "Dear Theodosia" at what point in his life?

- Opening night of "In the Heights"
- When his child was born
- When he got a dog
- When he married his wife

4. Continue the line: "I never thought I'd live past twenty."

- We say we live fast, reach for a glass, that's plenty.
- I'm lucky if I see more than one penny.
- Where I come from, some get half as many.
- I used to go out to drink with my friend Benny.

5. In the original Broadway cast, King George the Third was played by Jonathan Groff.

- True
- False

6. In the opening song, who says "I fought with him"?

- George Washington
- Madison/Hamilton
- Jefferson/Lafayette
- Peggy/Maria

7. In the original Broadway cast, Jasmine Cephas-Jones plays which Schuyler sister?

- Maria
- Angelica
- Peggy
- Eliza

8. What is George Washington's favorite line of scripture?

- Everyone will sit under their own vine and under their own fig tree.
- Love is patient, love is kind.
- For God so loved the world that he gave his one and only Son, that whoever believes in him shall not perish but have eternal

life.

- The LORD is my shepherd, I shall not be in want.

9. What compliment does Laurens get in "My Shot"?

- I think your pants look hot

- Let's get this guy in front of a crowd!

- Hard rock like Lancelot

- I like you a lot

10. There is real-life evidence that Eliza Schuyler burned the letters between herself and her husband.

- True
- False

11. Name the song from which these lyrics come: "Now you call me "amoral,"/ A "dangerous disgrace,"/ If you've got something to say/ Name a time and place/ Face to face"...

- Your Obedient Servant
- Cabinet Battle #2
- A Winter's Ball
- Cabinet Battle #1

12. Which ensemble member got to wear the Gypsy Robe on opening night?

- Carleigh Bettiol
- Gregory Haney
- Ariana DeBose
- Betsy Struxness

13. Which of these shows only had any of its cast or crew members participate in a Ham4Ham after the show had closed?

- RENT
- Fun Home
- Les Miserables
- Fiddler on the Roof

14. Complete the quote: "Heed not the rabble who scream 'revolution!'..."

- The revolution's coming- the have-nots will win this
- Oh my god, tear this dude apart
- They have not your interests at heart
- Chaos and bloodshed are not a solution

15. Which celebrity did NOT see "Hamilton" at some point in time?

- Kanye West and Kim Kardashian
- Beyonce and Jay-Z

- President Obama (and his family)
- David Bowie

ANSWER:

1.

The correct answer was Wait for It

"Wait for It" is sung by Aaron Burr, who was played by Leslie Odom Jr in the original Broadway cast.

2.

The correct answer was $10

Not only do cast members from "Hamilton" perform at the outdoor (and sometimes online) Ham4Ham shows - cast members from nearby musicals such as "Fun Home" and "Les Mis" have also participated in raffling off Hamilton tickets!

3.

Answer: When he got a dog

This isn't the full story - Lin says in "Hamilton: a Revolution" that already they had been struggling when they went to a vacation to the Dominican Republic with his wife's family. "My wife's aunt [...] was struggling was ALS, so the air was heavy: we dreaded/anticipated the news of her passing even as we attempted to make the best of this vacation. Amidst all this, one day a tiny stray puppy jumped up on my wife's beach chair and nipped at her ankle, with large brown eyes that pleaded, "Get me off this island." [...] Vanessa, a lifelong cat person, switched teams in that moment and Tobillo (Spanish for ankle) entered our lives for good."

4.

Answer: Where I come from, some get half as many.

Cast member Anthony Ramos (John Laurens / Phillip Schuyler) said that he related to this quote. In the neighborhood where he grew up, it was considered lucky to live past the age of 21 because so few did.

5.

Answer: True

At first, the role was given to Brian D'Arcy James. After several rehearsals, however, it was passed on to "Groffsauce", as he has been dubbed by both Mr. Miranda and the fandom.

6.

The correct answer was Jefferson/Lafayette

This is said together by Jefferson/Lafayette and Madison/Mulligan. Interestingly enough, the double casting is totally intentional. While Jefferson fought against Hamilton, Lafayette fought alongside him.

7.

Answer: Angelica

The correct answer was Peggy

She plays Maria Reynolds (hence the "I loved him" in the opening scene alongside Angelica and Eliza).

8.

Answer: Love is patient, love is kind.

The correct answer was Everyone will sit under their own vine and under their own fig tree.

He apparently quoted the line often while he was alive. Lin-Manuel Miranda didn't know this until he was personally informed by Hamilton's biographer, and he decided to put the line into the musical.

9.

The correct answer was I like you a lot

Just before this compliment to Laurens, he sang, "Mister Lafayette, hard rock like Lancelot, I think your pants look hot." The fact that Hamilton takes less than a moment to come up with personalized comments and then moves on to making revolutionary plans ("... A bunch of revolutionary manumission abolitionists?/ Give me a position, show me where the ammunition is!") is yet one more example of his rapid-fire thought.

10.

Answer: False

This is a nod to the clear lack of letters and documents. Lin tried to imagine why this was, and came up with the song "Burn", describing how Eliza went after her husband's legacy - the thing he treasured above all else - after he made his affair with Maria Reynolds public. A Ron Chernow's biography of Hamilton asserts that she burned her letters to him, but it is that author's opinion, not a fact that was documented at the time. All we have as evidence is a lack of correspondence.

11.

The correct answer was Your Obedient Servant

"Your Obedient Servant" is a shout-out to the way people back then signed their letters (the equivalent of 'sincerely'). This line is also used ironically, since "your obedient servant" implies civility while the song is an argument between Hamilton and Burr.

12.

Answer: Betsy Struxness

The Gypsy Robe is a theater tradition in which a chorus member with the most Broadway credits receives a robe on opening night. Before curtain, everyone associated with the show gather onstage for the Gypsy Robe ceremony.

13.

Answer: RENT

"RENT" tells the story of a group of starving young artists struggling to survive and create a life in New York City in the thriving days of Bohemian Alphabet City during the HIV/AIDS epidemic. It ran on Broadway from 1996 to 2008, closing before "Hamilton" opened.

14.

The correct answer was They have not your interests at heart

The song "Farmer Refuted" is based on an anonymously published pamphlet by Samuel Seabury signed, "A Westchester Farmer". Hamilton's responses were "A Full Vindication of the Measures of Congress" and "The Farmer Refuted".

15.

The correct answer was David Bowie

Many, many famous people- from Emma Watson to Bernie Sanders have seen this show (and loved it!). The Obamas liked it so much that they invited the cast over to the White House to perform. But David Bowie never saw it before his death in 2016

Things You Might Not Have Known About Hamilton

1. HAMILTON WAS INSPIRED BY RON CHERNOW'S BIOGRAPHY OF ALEXANDER HAMILTON.

Not long after his show In the Heights won four Tony Awards in 2008, Lin-Manuel Miranda went on vacation. Before he left, he picked up a biography called Alexander Hamilton. "I was just browsing the biography section. It could have been Truman," he told 60 Minutes. "I got to the part where a hurricane destroys St. Croix, where Hamilton is living. And he writes a poem about the carnage and this poem gets him off the island."

"That is part and parcel with the hip-hop narrative: writing your way out of your circumstances, writing the future you want to see for yourself," Miranda told The New York Times. "This is a guy who wrote at 14, 'I wish there was a war.' It doesn't get more hip-hop than that."

Miranda recalled to Vogue that "I Googled 'Alexander Hamilton hip-hop musical' and totally expected to see that someone had already written it. But no. So I got to work."

2. IT TOOK MIRANDA A YEAR TO WRITE HAMILTON'S FIRST SONG—AND ANOTHER YEAR TO WRITE THE SECOND SONG.

He performed the song, "Alexander Hamilton," at the White House in 2009 (you can watch the video above). "From what I hear," Questlove, who produced the cast album, told Billboard, "the president won't cease to let you know that: 'The White House is where it began.'"

It took Miranda another year to craft Hamilton's anthem, "My Shot." "Every couplet needed to be the best couplet I ever wrote," Miranda told 60 Minutes. "That's how seriously I was taking it."

3. MIRANDA WROTE HAMILTON'S LYRICS ON THE MOVE.

When he needed to come up with lyrics, he told Smithsonian, he walked. "For Hamilton what I'd do is write at the piano until I had something I liked," he said. "I'd make a loop of it and put it in my headphones and then walk around until I had the lyrics. That's where the notebooks come in, sort of write what comes to me, bring it back to the piano. I kind of need to be ambulatory to write lyrics."

4. HAMILTON STARTED AS A MIXTAPE, NOT A MUSICAL.

Initially, Miranda said he was working on a concept album inspired by the life of Alexander Hamilton called The Hamilton Mixtape. "I always had an eye toward the stage for the story of Hamilton's life, but I began with the idea of a concept album, the way Andrew Lloyd Webber's Evita and Jesus Christ Superstar were albums before they were musicals," Miranda recounted to the Hollywood Reporter. "And I built this score by dream casting my favorite artists. I always imagined George Washington as a mix between Common and John Legend (a pretty good description of Christopher Jackson, actually, who plays our first president); Hercules Mulligan was Busta Rhymes; and Hamilton was modeled after my favorite polysyllabic rhyming heroes, Rakim, Big Pun, and Eminem."

The reason, he told The New York Times, was because "I wanted to be a little more selfish with this—I wanted the lyrics to have the density that my favorite hip-hop albums have … It was easier to think of it as a hip-hop album, because then I could really just pack the lyrics. [But] I only know how to write musicals." He performed

12 musical numbers from The Hamilton Mixtape at Lincoln Center's American Songbook series in January 2012; he began workshopping the show in 2014. It played The Public beginning in January 2015 and made the jump to Broadway in July 2015 (it officially opened in August).

5. MIRANDA DID HIS RESEARCH—BOTH HISTORICALLY AND MUSICALLY—TO WRITE HAMILTON.

In addition to reading Chernow's biography of Hamilton, Miranda read Hamilton's letters and works and visited sites important to the American Revolution in New York City. He explained to The Atlantic that, to understand Burr, he read The Heartbreak of Aaron Burr by H.W. Brands, and to nail the dueling code of the day, he picked up Affairs of Honor by Joanne Freeman. He wrote, for a time, at the Morris-Jumel Mansion, which Washington once used as a headquarters during the Revolutionary War. In October 2014, before the show began playing at The Public, he and director Thomas Kail went to the Weehawken, New Jersey, dueling ground where Burr shot Hamilton (the actual dueling grounds are covered by train tracks now, but there is a small memorial there).

Miranda also looked at other musicals before diving into Hamilton, like Jesus Christ Superstar and Les Miserables. "I really got my Les Miz on in this score, like being really smart about where to reintroduce a theme," he told The New Yorker. "In terms of how it accesses your tear ducts, nothing does it better than that show."

6. RON CHERNOW WAS A HISTORICAL CONSULTANT FOR HAMILTON.

Miranda met Chernow before he performed the song that would become "Alexander Hamilton" at the White House (in fact, he sang the song to Chernow in the biographer's living room), and soon Chernow became a consultant on the show. "[Miranda] was smart enough to know that the best way to dramatize this story was to stick as close to the facts as possible," Chernow told 60 Minutes.

"I'm theater people, and theater people, the only history they know is the history they know from other plays and musicals," Miranda told The Atlantic. "So to that end, I felt an enormous responsibility to be as historically accurate as possible, while still telling the most dramatic story possible. And that's why Ron Chernow is a historical consultant on the thing, and, you know, he was always sort of keeping us honest. And when I did part from the historical record or take dramatic license, I made sure I was able to defend it to Ron, because I knew that I was going to have to defend it in the real world. None of those choices are made lightly."

According to Smithsonian, Chernow looked at every draft and every song and assessed everything for accuracy.

7. HAMILTON WASN'T ALWAYS SUNG THROUGH.

Hamilton is sung and rapped from start to finish, but it wasn't always that way. "We actually went down the road with a playwright," Miranda told Grantland. "There's a version of Act 1 where we had songs and they were the songs that are in the show, but we found that if you start with our opening number, you can't go back to speech. The ball is just thrown too high in the air."

8. ONE SCENE FROM HAMILTON DIDN'T MAKE IT ONTO THE SOUNDTRACK.

The show features one scene that isn't sung, and which Miranda kept off of the cast album: In "Tomorrow There'll Be More of Us," which takes place between "Dear Theodosia" and "Non-Stop," Hamilton finds out that his friend Laurens has been killed. "I made a decision not to record this scene on the album, for two reasons," Miranda wrote on Tumblr:

"1) It really is more of a scene than a song, the only SCENE in our show, and I think its impact is at its fullest in production form. 2) As someone who grew up ONLY listening to cast albums (we ain't have money for a lot of Broadway shows, like most people) those withheld moments were REVELATIONS to me when I finally experienced them onstage, years later. Hamilton is sung through, and I wanted to have at least ONE revelation in store for you. I stand by the decision, and I think the album is better for it."

9. MIRANDA WROTE KING GEORGE'S SONG IN

HAMILTON, "YOU'LL BE BACK," ON HIS HONEYMOON.

Because he's an interloper on the proceedings of Hamilton, King George's song, "You'll Be Back," is quite different from the rest of the show's numbers. "It's a throwback to a sixties Beatles tune," Jonathan Groff, who plays King George, told Vogue. "And it's a breakup song between America and England, which is fabulous. He's like, 'You're leaving me? Oh, really? Well, good luck with that.'" Miranda wrote the song while on his honeymoon in 2010 "without a piano around," he told Grantland.

10. THE ORIGINAL VERSION OF THE HAMILTON SONG "MY SHOT" HAD AN EXTRA VERSE FOR HERCULES MULLIGAN.

"I'm Hercules Mulligan, a tailor spying on the British Government / I take the measurements, information and then I smuggle it / Up to my brother's revolutionary covenant / I'm running with the Sons of Liberty, and I'm loving it," Mulligan raps. At that point, neither the Marquis de Lafayette nor John Laurens were part of the song. You can hear the rest of the demo here; portions of Mulligan's verse ended up in "Yorktown (World Turned Upside Down)."

Printed in Great Britain
by Amazon

54941443R00040